For Zoey and every child with a Dream

Never let anything get in your way of pursuing it!

Most Sincere Thanks!

Zoey and Melissa – nothing without you
*(I don't know how others achieve Dreams without the support of a family like you,
I know I wouldn't have... my love forever!)*

Bob – from my heart, my friend, WOW!
*(your mind, skill, and patience with me turned my Dream into
the reality that is the Zack and Zoey Adventures™ brand)*

Ron Sparkman, Stardom
www.stardomspace.com
(this book and what comes after are better for your involvement)

Space Foundation Discovery Center
www.discoverspace.org
(museum staffs are precious gems - hiding in plain sight)

"Welcome back!"

"This is Lauren McDonald and we're back to our interview with Zack and Zoey, the brother and sister team behind the best project ever, what they call 'Project KESSEL.'

Before the break, we learned Project KESSEL is the 'Kids Entire Solar System Experimentation Lab.' Zoey, you were saying there were some huge challenges in getting this project built.

Please tell us the rest of that story."

Zoey began, "Ok, Lauren. We'd added Aaron and Kaitlyn to our team, but we were having problem after problem..."

The team's list of problems was long:

"We can't build a solar system without gas giants," said Zoey, "but I have no idea how to create them in our back yard."

"Aaron and I know what we need for our 'Mars Yard.' We even designed it," Zack explained, "but without any money, we don't know how to build it."

"Rockets," Aaron added with frustration, "we can't say we have an 'entire solar system lab' without rockets, which aren't even in our plans."

Kaitlyn also spoke up, "We formed this Project Team to win the class prize, but I don't think our idea of a project poster is enough to win. It's a little boring."

As the team leader, Zoey took charge, "Let's all do some more research and see if we can find any solutions."

The team got back to work...

"Hey guys, check this out," Zack said pointing to his tablet, "while researching Mars rovers, I found this space website which is holding a contest for kids creating space projects... that's us!"

"What's the website?" Zoey asked.

"It's called Stardom," Zack answered.

Aaron asked, "What's their contest?"

"It says 'a huge Grand Prize to the winning team,'" Zack explained, "but it doesn't say what the prize is."

"That sounds awesome," Aaron said, "it would be cool to win a huge Grand Prize!"

"How do we enter their contest?" Zoey asked.

"Here it is," Zack read off the website, "'Upload a video, three minutes or less, to our social media page introducing your team and explaining your project.'"

"Hey!" Kaitlyn nearly shouted. "That's the solution to how we win the class prize. Let's ask Jen to join our team. She's a video wiz, so we can make Project KESSEL into a video presentation, too!"

"Great idea," Zoey said.

"I'm going to text her right now," Kaitlyn said. "Ok... Jen's in!"

"And..." Aaron said with a sly grin, "what would be a more awesome way to begin our Project KESSEL video than with a rocket launch?"

Zack knew just what Aaron was thinking, "Yes! Let's make Reima the last member of our team, he's already doing his project on rockets."

"Hey Zoey," said Mom, "how is your team doing on your project?"

"Hey Mom," Zoey began quietly, "I came in to ask you a couple things."

"What is it, sweetheart?"

"Zack found this website called Stardom. They're holding a contest for kids making space projects, but we need your permission to enter our video for their contest. Can we... please?"

"That sounds ok to me," Mom answered, "just show me the website before you do, deal?"

"Deal! The other thing is that we don't have money, so Zack and Aaron don't know how they're going to build our Mars Yard. Any ideas?"

After thinking for a moment, Mom replied, "Mars is the red planet, right?"

"Yes," Zoey agreed.

"We do live in Colorado," Mom continued, "there's red rocks everywhere, tell Zack and Aaron I'll bring them out with a couple of buckets to collect what they need?"

"That would be perfect," Zoey exclaimed. "thanks, Mom!"

Zoey continued, "Since you have great ideas, Mom, do you have any ideas on how we can include gas giants in our project? I'm stumped."

Mom thought, "I don't, but didn't you say you met a genius on gas giants on your field trip to the Discovery Center?"

"We did," Zoey agreed.

"I don't have any ideas for gas giants, but I can drive you to the Discovery Center. Maybe you can ask him if he has any ideas for you."

"Thank you, Mom, thank you!" said Zoey. "I'll email Elias now with my question."

"Obviously, you can't get a Science on a Sphere® in your backyard, Zoey," explained Elias, "but I do have a good solution for you to be able to add gas giants into Project KESSEL."

"That's great, Elias, what is it?"

"Bubbles."

"Bubbles?!?" asked Zoey with raised eyebrows.

"Bubbles are actually one of the ways real scientists study the atmospheres of gas giants in their laboratories," explained Elias.

"No way," exclaimed Zoey, "I can definitely do bubbles... thanks, Elias!"

Reima got right to work the day he joined the team, "With just a little more work, our rocket launch pad will be ready," he said.

"Our gas giant area is ready," Kaitlyn said, "so I hope Zoey gets a solution at the Discovery Center today."

"Thanks to Zack's Mom," Aaron explained, "we got enough red rocks and dirt to build our Mars yard. It should be finished tomorrow."

"Thanks again, Elias," said Zoey, "this solution is really going to help us win that Grand Prize."

"What Grand Prize?" asked Elias. "I thought this was for a school project."

"It is," explained Zoey, "but we found this website called Stardom, and they're awarding a huge Grand Prize to the best space project created by kids, so we're entering their contest."

"In that case, do I have a big surprise for you, Zoey!" said Elias with a smile. "Ron, the Founder of Stardom, is here right now, he works with us. Do you want to meet him?"

"Yes, I do!" exclaimed Zoey.

"Hey Ron," said Elias, "this is Zoey. She's been in for field trips before and she just told me her project team is entering your Stardom contest."

"That's cool! Hi Zoey, I'm Ron. It's great to meet you. I'm excited you're entering our contest. What's the topic of your project?"

"We call it Project KESSEL."

"KESSEL," Ron said with excitement, "like the Kessel Run in Star Wars?"

"Yes, exactly!"

"I love that," said Ron, "I look forward to seeing your team's video. It was nice to meet you."

"You, too, and thanks!" said Zoey.

"Hey team, gather around," Zoey said, "I have some amazing news."

"What's up, Zoey," Kaitlyn asked. "did you get a solution on how to add gas giants to the project?"

"Actually I did... but I have even bigger news..."

"Don't make us wait," asked Zack impatiently,
"what is it?!"

"While I was at the Discovery Center, I met Ron, the founder of Stardom!"

"What, really?!" Aaron said.

"Yeah, and get this, he told me he's excited about seeing our project video!"

"That's so cool," Zack said excitedly, "let's get back to work to make sure we really make this the best project ever!"

"Wow, Zoey," Lauren continued the interview, "at this point, it sounds like things were going really well for your team."

"They were, until..." Zoey's voice trailed off.

"Until," Zack continued for her, "Jen reminded us we'd completely forgotten to build our scale model solar system."

Zoey finished, "That's a centerpiece of our Kids Entire Solar System Experimentation Lab. Here's what happened..."

"Ok guys," Jen began, "now that we are close to completing each of our areas, I'll be going around filming everything for our project video."

"Ok," the team agreed.

Jen continued, "Unless I'm talking to you directly, just ignore me and the camera and keep doing what you're doing."

"I think I'll start my filming with our Project KESSEL poster," Jen said, "it's the one piece that shows our entire project."

"Good idea, Jen," said Zoey.

As Jen began filming, Aaron said "Reima is out back constructing our rocket launch pad, so we can do this meeting without him."

"We found solutions to each of our problems," Zoey said, "now we need to finish getting our entire project together in time."

"Hey guys," Jen said looking worried, "I think we have a problem."

"What's the problem?" asked Zoey.

"The scale model of the solar system is one of the centerpieces of our whole project," explained Jen, "but we haven't built it yet."

"Oh man, we nearly forgot," Zack said.

"It's ok, Jen," Kaitlyn answered calmly, "we'd already collected the spheres we need, and after I finished designing our project poster, I started painting the planets."

"Check these out," Aaron said holding an armful of colorful planets.

As Jen filmed, Zack narrated for the video, "When entering our Mars Yard, you can immediately see our first Mars Habitat being built and the tracks our rover has been making as we explore the surface of the red planet."

Zoey continued the narration, "Our rocket engineer, Reima, is busy preparing our launch pad, and I'm finalizing our gas giant zone, where we can study gas giant atmospheres in the swirls of bubbles."

"Project KESSEL includes rockets to launch, rovers to explore rocky planets and moons, a gas giant study area, and a complete scale model of the solar system," Zack explained.

"You'll see it all in our video," said Jen.

"Wow team," began Lauren, "that's quite a story!
We all know you won your class prize, which was being interviewed here on *News 99* with me... but now I have a surprise for you."

Lauren paused, then said, "Come on out!"

"Hi Zoey, hey team! I'm Ron Sparkman. I'm here to announce that Project KESSEL is the winner of our first ever Kids' Space Project contest!"

"YES!" the team shouted together.

"We LOVED your entire solar system lab and your example to all of us that when we reach for the stars, great things can happen!
We designed this Grand Prize just for your team. It's enough rockets, drones, and rovers to expand Project KESSEL for you to help kids learn more about our solar system."

"Great job," Ron said, "congratulations!"

REMOTE CONTROL
DRONE

Hey Adventurers!

We're not done with Project KESSEL...
Learning about space, our solar system, and space exploration is exciting
and we want to make it more hands on for kids like YOU!

THE HUMAN ADVENTURE

IS JUST BEGINNING...

MAKE A SCALE MODEL

A Zack and Zoey ACTIVITY

MATERIALS:
3 lbs of clay or dough Pen
Paper Ruler (optional)

1. Write the name of each of the nine planets on separate pieces of paper. Spread the labeled papers out on a table. This is where you will be placing the clay to make each of the planets.

2. Make 10 equal balls.

3. Squash 6 of them together...this will be JUPITER. Place the ball on the paper labeled JUPITER

4. Take another 3 and squash them together...this is only part of SATURN (more will be added to SATURN). Place the ball on t he paper labeled SATURN.

5. Divide the ball of clay that is left into 10. Squash 5 of them together and add them to SATURN.

6. Take another 2 and squash them together...this is URANUS. Place the ball on the paper labeled URANUS.

7. Take 2 and squash them together...this is NEPTUNE. Place the ball on the paper labeled NEPTUNE.

8. With the ball that is left, make 10 equal sized balls. Squash 9 of them together...add them to SATURN. SATURN is now complete!

9. Divide the remaining ball into 2. 1 is EARTH. Place the ball on the paper labeled EARTH.

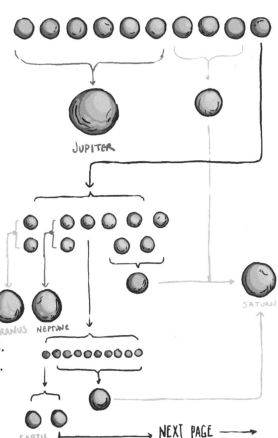

JUPITER

URANUS NEPTUNE

SATURN

EARTH NEXT PAGE →

OF THE SOLAR SYSTEM

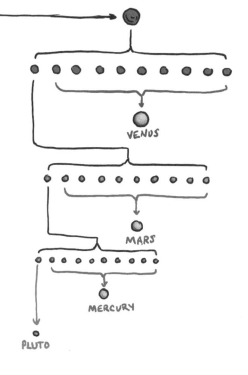

10. Now is when things get tricky! Divide the ball that is left into 10. 9 of them make up VENUS. Place the ball on the paper labeled VENUS.

11. Make 10 balls out of the 1 that is left again. Use 9 to make MARS. Place the ball on the paper labeled MARS.

12. Divide the ball of dough that is left into 10. 9 of them make up MERCURY (Place them on the paper labeled MERCURY)

13. The last tiny ball left is PLUTO! Place the ball on the paper labeled PLUTO.

Why isn't the Sun included in this activity? The Sun is so much larger than all of the planets that if you use a 3lb tub of clay to make the planets and Pluto, it would take 980 tubs to make the Sun!

CPSIA information can be obtained
at www.ICGtesting.com
Printed in the USA
LVHW070052160819
627842LV00002B/3/P